THE 'DREADNOUG

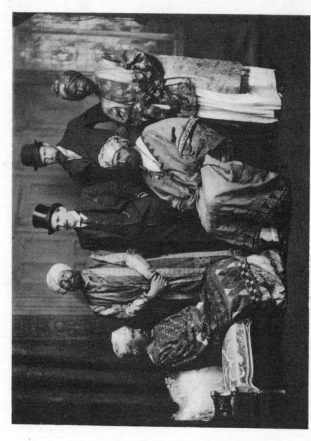

'THE EMPEROR OF ABYSSINIA' AND HIS SUITE

Names from left to right:

Virginia Stephen (Virginia Woolf), Duncan Grant, Horace Cole

THE 'DREADNOUGHT' HOAX

ADRIAN STEPHEN

WITH AN INTRODUCTION BY
QUENTIN BELL

CHATTO & WINDUS

THE HOGARTH PRESS
LONDON

Published in 1983 by
Chatto & Windus · The Hogarth Press
40 William IV Street
London WC2N 4DF

First published 1936
Reissued, with an introduction by
Quentin Bell 1983

British Library Cataloguing in Publication Data

Stephen, Adrian
The dreadnought hoax.
I. Title   II. Bell, Quentin
823′.912 [F]   PR6037.T/

ISBN 0 7011 2747 3

Printed in Great Britain by
Redwood Burn Ltd
Trowbridge, Wiltshire

ILLUSTRATIONS

INTRODUCTION

"Could you be so good, Sir, as to hold the end of this tape for a few minutes?"

"But of course". The responsible citizen is only too glad to be of service to the official-looking stranger. He takes up his post holding his end of the tape with becoming gravity; he can hold a tape with the best of them; he has a proper sense of public duty and, perhaps, of his own importance.

Meanwhile the official-looking stranger has gone round the corner paying out measured tape behind him until he is well out of sight. Presently he happens upon another responsible-looking citizen.

"Could you be so kind, Sir . . ."

And then, says the legend, for we are in a world of myth and semi-myth, the official-looking gentleman slips away to a point of vantage from which he can survey his victims. Half an hour later each is still holding his end of the tape, both are still grave and resolute but increasingly conscious that something has gone wrong.

The official-looking stranger is the anti-hero of this little book, Horace de Vere Cole. This and many other stories of public mischief have gathered around his name as a dog gathers burrs. The number of hoaxes and deceptions with which he is credited is prodigious and some of them are surely untrue; but his fame rests upon the great *Dreadnought* Hoax, which was indeed his work. It was a nine days wonder; it was noticed and embroidered in the press, it resulted in questions in Parliament, it is said to have led to a revision of the security regulations of the Royal Navy. It was a source of endless merriment and some indignation. Many years later, in a sailors' café in Toulon there was a stir of excitement when it became known that one of the customers, Mr Duncan Grant, had taken a part in the hoax. The story was a dearly cherished memory of the French Navy. It gave Cole what he had always wanted – fame, or at least notoriety, and, because some of the participants were later to achieve celebrity, a lasting place in the chronicles of the time. He did little else during his lifetime but he did once contribute to the gaiety of nations.

This account of the *Dreadnought* escapade and of the Sultan of Zanzibar's visit to Cambridge, which was as it were a dress rehearsal for the visit to the fleet, was written by Adrian Stephen in 1936 after the death of Cole. Adrian, it might have seemed, was disqualified by nature for any venture involving the use of disguise. He was immensely tall with an unforgettable voice and manner; one could, so one would have supposed, spot him in a crowd at a distance of two thousand yards. In fact, as will be seen, his powers of deception were remarkable; moreover he had a quality which was most serviceable in what was at times a nerve-racking undertaking; he was, or at least could be, sublimely imperturbable. I have seen him sailing a boat under circumstances which would have perturbed almost anyone else, and with this coolness went a dry, half melancholy humour. Living with, teased by and teasing a very imaginative sister, he cultivated a very matter of fact style and this is evident in the following pages which have the great merit of treating what is in many ways a fantastic subject with sobriety and with an evident desire to tell the truth in unpretentious language. It is far and away the best and most reliable account of what took place and one is grateful for it. But, at the same time, it is impossible not to regret that it is now the only first-hand document. Virginia Woolf did once write and deliver a lecture on the subject. It was written during the summer of the year 1940 for the benefit of the Women's Institute in Rodmell; it was repeated to a smaller audience a few weeks later. I heard it.

I wish I had the kind of memory that enables one to draw such things intact from the past. As it is I can only confirm the report of E. M. Forster: it left us 'helpless with laughter'. Three typescript pages remain and these I have published elsewhere.[1] I can, in addition recall something of the end of that lecture. Virginia who had taken her part in the conspiracy, described her return home, still turbaned and berobed, still with the remnants of grease paint and a beard upon her face to be greeted by her astonished cook, Sophy Farrell, with the words: 'Oh Miss Genia, Miss Genia!'

It is worth noting the manner in which

[1] *Virginia Woolf: a biography*, Volume One, Appendix E.

Virginia Stephen, as she then was, became involved in the hoax. The Emperor of Abyssinia had to be provided with a suite; as the day of the exploit approached this suite began to melt away until only two persons remained; for an emperor this seemed insufficient. Virginia was asked to take part and, at very short notice, accepted. Her sister Vanessa was horrified, she was sure that the plan would fail; if it had the Abyssinians might have suffered some pretty rough treatment, an ordeal for which Virginia had neither the psychological nor the bodily strength.

Such fears were surely justified. Looking at Adrian Stephen's account it is hard to see how such a hoax could succeed. In many of the newspaper accounts we are told of elaborate and painstaking efforts taken by the conspirators successfully to deceive the navy. Nothing could be further from the truth. The only merit of the plan, in so far as there was a plan, lay in its pure lunatic audacity.

A few years earlier an elderly German criminal dressed up as a Prussian officer, took command of a platoon of soldiers, descended upon the little town of Köpenick and there, having seized the town hall by a show of armed strength, arrested the Bürgermeister and appropriated documents. His proceedings filled Europe with a horrid joy and may even have inspired the Abyssinians, although Adrian Stephen seems to believe that theirs was the earlier deception. In the only account that I have seen of that affair (and it was long ago) the criminal is represented as carefully studying Prussian drill books and Prussian regulations and as making himself complete master of every detail and every difficulty that he might encounter. It would seem to be the sensible thing to do; anyone who was not crazy would do it, anyone that is who was not English.

Consider now the proceedings of Cole and his friends. In the Zanzibar hoax, at the end of a glorious day of civic junketting they were conducted to Cambridge Railway Station. They did not in the least want to go to London and they discovered that they had not made any plans for a getaway. What did they do? They gathered up their robes and ran, they ran until they found a cab and jumped into it. And supposing there had been no cab?

In their naval encounter they clearly made no enquiries concerning the appearance of Abyssinians; they gambled on the probability that their hosts would be as ignorant as they. Certainly they chose wisely in pretending to come from what was then a landlocked state, they relied upon a message *en clair* from someone who pretended to send a telegram from the Admiralty; they made the sketchiest arrangements at the last minute concerning the false names that they would use, they made a very half hearted effort to learn Swahili, imagining this to be the language of Abyssinia, they trusted to luck, to the inspiration of the moment and even their beards failed always to adhere to their chins. It is almost shocking that they should have been so completely successful whereas the poor Captain of Köpenick, who went in search of a passport, overlooking one tiny detail: that there were no passports in the offices which he had commandeered, was arrested and sent to prison. It seems unjust.

I suppose that there was a kind of valiant amateurishness about the British hoaxers which was matched by an equal degree of amateurishness in their dupes. We have all grown more solemn and serious and 'security conscious' and a part of the fun went out of life after 1914. One admires the light-hearted assurance that a joke is a joke which prompted Adrian to suggest to Cole that they also should take command of a platoon of German soldiers and march it over the French frontier; but it is hard to think that anyone would have suggested such a thing in later years.

Whether the sequel to the *Dreadnought* affair, with its ludicrous points of honour and formalised revenges, also belongs to the past I do not know. I hope so. Virginia Woolf, in that odd little story 'A Society', makes fun of these masculine absurdities and I think still had them in mind when she came to write *Three Guineas*. She had entered the Abyssinian adventure for the fun of the thing; but she came out of it with a new sense of the brutality and silliness of men. It must be said, however, that the gentle ironies of Adrian Stephen make the same point with telling effect.

Altogether it is a splendid story but perhaps it is not quite complete; there must be more evidence in official documents and in letters, even the newspapers and music halls of the time have not been properly examined. At a time when a multitude of dissertations are produced every year dealing with every conceivable aspect of Virginia Woolf's life and work it seems odd that no one should have examined the circumstances which led her to wear a turban and a beard and which brought her, for the first time, into contact with the National Press; such a study might be amusing, which would make a change, or might even lead to the rediscovery of the lost manuscript which would be splendid.

QUENTIN BELL

AUTHOR'S NOTE

In these pages I tell the story of some events mainly as I saw them myself. As I am the narrator perhaps the picture centres too much round me. I must say therefore that neither of the two hoaxes which I describe would have happened without Cole as ring-leader. Cole must take the lion's share of credit and, of course, of blame.

THE
'DREADNOUGHT'
HOAX

From time to time, and especially since Horace Cole died, there has arisen a queer stir of interest in what was once called the " *Dreadnought* Hoax," so it has been suggested that I should tell the true story.

"Why you?" is the obvious question, and it should be answered. I am not a literary person in any sense, and at least one of them involved in the hoax is so much better qualified in almost every way that it may seem that no answer is possible. I was inclined to think so myself, but it was pointed out that I had certain qualifications that were shared by no one. For one thing, I was the only person besides Horace Cole himself who took part both in this hoax and in another of which this was in a way the offspring ; but much more important is my habit of truth-telling, which makes it all but impossible for me to tell a lie. It was tactfully put to me that though it was true enough that others of the party might be more gifted and could make an infinitely more amusing legend than I, yet a legend their story would remain, while I, not having the imagination to invent an untruth, would be bound to stick to the facts. Anyhow I can assure any readers that it is the facts that they will get from me—with me they can feel safe from deception.

I do not know that any credit is due to the inventor of the hoax, probably most people would say not, but if any is due it should go to Horace Cole. It was he who invented the hoax which he and I and some others played when we were at Cambridge, and of which this was essentially a repetition. He and I were sitting in his rooms in

Trinity one evening and I suppose we must have been feeling depressed for I remember that we set ourselves to think out some plan of amusement. We had both already played a few hoaxes on a small scale, and it occurred to both of us that it might be amusing to do something more elaborate. His plan was the one that we adopted, partly because it would cost less money than mine, partly because it would be carried out immediately, and partly because he pooh-poohed mine as impracticable. I shall mention my plan all the same, even though we did not carry it out, for I think it throws an odd light on the world we lived in before the War, that so very quiet a being as myself should have made such a proposal seriously. I think now, too, that I was in the right, and that my plan could have been successful was later almost proved by the *Hauptmann von Köpenick*.

It had seemed to me ever since I was very young, just as I imagine it had seemed to Cole, that anyone who took up an attitude of authority over anyone else was necessarily also someone who offered a leg for everyone else to pull, and of all the institutions in the world that offered a leg for everyone's pulling the most obvious was the German Army. I think there had just been some trouble near the French frontier—I don't remember whether it was what was called the "Zabern incident" or whether that happened later, but anyhow I know that the time for one reason or another seemed "ripe."

My suggestion was simply that Cole and I should acquire the uniforms of German officers and take them with us to some town near the Franco-German frontier in Alsace-Lorraine. We were to choose a suitable neighbourhood for the purpose and then, putting on our uniforms, to take command of a detachment of troops and march with them across the frontier into France. Once we got across what happened would naturally have depended on circumstances. I had no doubt, of course, that the French would stop us before we had gone a kilometre. We should have surrendered immediately, and perhaps been interned, there would, I hoped, have been what is called an "international incident," the Kaiser would have made gestures and sent telegrams, and other people might have been amused.

I do not know that the plan was very brilliant, but I believe we could have carried it out even if nowadays one would surely think twice about doing so. I do not know either that if everyone shared my feelings towards the great armed forces of the world, the world would not be a happier place to live in. However, I don't pretend I had a moral to preach, I only felt that armies and suchlike bodies presented legs that were almost irresistible.

Cole's suggestion was easier and cheaper to carry out than mine, and accordingly we chose it. It happened that at this time the Sultan of Zanzibar was in England; what could be simpler than to impersonate him and pay a state visit to Cambridge?

As a matter of fact, when we thought things over we found one or two difficulties to deal with. For instance, a photograph of the real Sultan had appeared in the newspapers, and he was not in the least like either of us, and we decided accordingly to represent not himself, but his imaginary uncle instead. Then we wanted to avoid being sent down if possible, and we thought it better not to hoax the University authorities themselves—they would be more likely to be lenient if we were satisfied with hoaxing the Mayor. Also, as we meant to have a

'THE SULTAN OF ZANZIBAR' AND HIS SUITE

Names from left to right:

Adrian Stephen, – Bowen Colthurst, Horace Cole,
Leland Buxton, 'Drummer' Howard.

European interpreter with us we thought it wiser to get someone from Oxford—a Cambridge undergraduate would be in more danger of recognition.

A few days after we thought of the plan we carried it out. We collected two friends from Cambridge, and another from Oxford, went to London, and got made up at a theatrical costumier's. From London we took train back to Cambridge, first sending off a telegram to the Mayor warning him to expect us. We signed the telegram " Lucas," I remember, simply because someone said that high colonial officials always bore that name.

Anyhow, everything went off perfectly. We were met at the station by the Town Clerk and driven in a carriage to the Guildhall, where we were formally received by the Mayor. We then paid a royal visit to a charity bazaar which was going on there, Cole as the Sultan's uncle making enormous purchases at all the stalls, and then emerged into the town, where we were shown the principal colleges.

When all was over, the Town Clerk conducted us back to the station, and then arose the problem of escape, for we had no wish to return to London. We entered what was then the Great Eastern part of the station, but as soon as we reached the platform we lifted our skirts, fled through the crowds waiting for the train, out of the Great Northern entrance, jumped into hansoms and drove off. We just told the cabbies to drive for all they were worth, and directed them out into the country. Eventually we stopped at a point whence we could make our way across the fields to the house of some friends, and here we changed our clothes and had a much-needed wash and dinner before going back to our college.

This escapade became quite famous for a time, and a full account of it was published in the *Daily Mail*. Cole was strongly in favour of publishing our story, but the rest of us were against it. We had had our fun, and it seemed a little like gloating over our victims. However, whatever the rest of us thought, Cole said he was determined to go to London and see what he could do to get " publicity," and I decided to go with him to see that, at any rate, what got published was the truth.

The *Daily Mail* listened to us, sent down an investigator to Cambridge to test our story, and eventually published a full report. It soon leaked out, of course, who the hoaxers were, and I was told later on by the Master of one of the colleges that the Mayor of Cambridge had asked the Vice-Chancellor to send us down. The Vice-Chancellor replied, I believe, that he would send us down if the Mayor insisted, but he advised the Mayor for the sake of his own reputation to think it over. In the end nothing happened to us, every-thing blew over and the hoax was generally felt to be amusing even by people who hotly disapproved of the later hoax on the Navy. The person hoaxed was only a Cambridge tradesman (he kept a chemist's shop), whereas naval officers, as one critic said, were " different "—they were " men of honour."

The " *Dreadnought* Hoax " was in its main plan a repetition of the other, and took place a few years later. The " Chan-nel Fleet " (I believe it was called this) was then lying at Weymouth under the com-mand of Admiral X, whose flagship was the *Dreadnought*, and, in short, we proposed to visit it in the characters of the Emperor of Abyssinia and his suite. The idea was suggested to Cole by a naval officer as a matter of fact, and those who made a to-do

29

H.M.S. *Dreadnought*, the ninth of its name
in the Royal Navy, 1906–20

about the honour of the Navy would have been interested to hear this. I am afraid I may be letting something out of the bag, too, if I say that one of his first aims was to pull the leg of another naval officer, a cousin of my own. My cousin was chief of the Admiral's staff at that time and so might be considered to be involved.

Cole asked me to meet his friend at luncheon, and he and I took to the plan at once, and the next thing was to collect our troupe of hoaxers. Cole got hold of two friends, Mr. Anthony Buxton and Mr. Guy Ridley, and I got hold of my sister Virginia, now Mrs. Woolf, and Mr. Duncan Grant.

The plan which had worked so well at Cambridge was to be repeated as nearly as possible, but this time Cole was to be a young gentleman from the Foreign Office, Buxton was to be the Emperor of Abyssinia, Virginia, Guy Ridley and Duncan Grant were to form the suite, and I was to be the interpreter.

Virginia and I lived in Fitzroy Square in those days, and it was arranged that the whole troupe should meet in our house early one morning to be made up for their parts. Clarksons undertook to dress us up, and I believe the great Mr. Willy Clarkson himself came to superintend, though, of course, we let no one into our plot. Horace Cole just had to wear a top-hat and tail coat, but the Emperor and his suite, including Virginia, had to have their faces blackened, to wear false beards and moustaches and elaborate Eastern robes. I was merely disguised with a false beard, a moustache and a little sunburn powder. I wore a bowler hat and a great coat and looked, I am afraid, like a seedy commercial traveller.

When all was ready we took taxis to Paddington Station and got into a train with a luncheon car bound for Weymouth. The telegram, warning the Admiral to expect us, was to be sent off after we started, and it was to be signed "Hardinge," though the friend who sent it was named in sober fact Tudor Castle. Hardinge, however, was the name of the permanent head of the Foreign Office.

There is little to tell of the journey down. Cole and I insisted that the others should not go with us into the luncheon car, as we were afraid of accidents to their make-up. He and I went and lunched together, however, and spent our time largely in the attempt to teach me the Swahili language. Swahili is, I believe, spoken in some parts of East Africa. Whether it is spoken in Abyssinia or not I don't know, but we thought it might be as well for me to know a few phrases, and to that end we had bought a grammar from the Society for the Propagation of the Gospel. Of course, when the time came, I could hardly remember two words, though some newspapers later described us as having talked " fluent Abyssinian." However, if it did nothing else, the study of Swahili helped Cole and me, at any rate, to pass the time, for to tell the truth we were feeling rather nervous. Something might so easily go wrong. It might be that the telegram ought to have been written in some special code, or it might be that the Admiral would send a message by wireless to get it confirmed, or perhaps my cousin might recognize me (he would hardly recognize Virginia) and then we should get into trouble.

I think that perhaps the most exciting moment for me that day was first the arrival at Weymouth—that was the plunge into the cold bath. As the train slowed down for the station we were all agog. I think I half expected that no notice would be taken of us at all, and we should just have to slink back to London but no, there on the platform stood a naval officer in full uniform, and the hoax had begun.

As we got out of the train the officer stepped smartly up and saluted the Emperor formally, and Cole and I made whatever introductions seemed necessary.

In spite of the short notice we had given, everything was ready for our reception. Inside the station a red carpet was laid down for us to walk on, and there was a barrier in position to keep sightseers at a proper distance. Outside we were conducted to cabs which took us down to the harbour and there, again, was the smart little steam launch which was to take us out to the Fleet.

By the time we reached the *Dreadnought* the expedition had become for me at any rate almost an affair of every day. It was hardly a question any longer of a hoax. We were almost acting the truth. Everyone was expecting us to act as the Emperor and his suite, and it would have been extremely difficult not to.

It may have seemed to some an odd introduction to the story of a hoax in which I took part to say that I am incapable of deception. Of course, I did not mean the words to be taken too pedantically. Suppose someone sent word to an unwelcome visitor that he was not at home you could hardly on that ground describe him as a liar without being so misleading as to be guilty of falsehood yourself. Pedantically speaking, he would, of course, be a liar, and, pedantically speaking, I must admit myself capable of deception when I took part in the hoax. But once the telegram had been sent off, and we had arrived and been received, it would not have been an easy matter to tell the truth, and we almost, I think, believed in the hoax ourselves.

We steamed out then in our little brass-funnelled launch into the bay where we saw the *Dreadnought* lying among the Fleet, with lines of marines drawn up on her deck and flags flying from her mast. Then, as we came alongside and approached the ship's gangway, the band struck up its music.

As a matter of fact, the ship was smaller than I expected, I remember, and uglier, with its funnels and its great tripod mast and its gun turrets and what not, stuck all about. However, I had not much time for criticism. When we arrived the Admiral and his staff and the captain of the ship, all in their gold-laced uniforms, were ready to receive us.

Cole went on board first, I think, and then the Emperor and his suite, and I was last. I had one or two surprises at this

point. Cole was performing the introductions, and I was a little taken aback to
hear myself introduced as Kauffmann.
We had all chosen our own names coming
down in the train and Cole, who was
rather deaf, had misheard me. I had
chosen an English name that sounded a
little like Kauffmann and Kauffmann
with a German name I was to be. I was
a little alarmed at this, because German
spy scares were for ever being started in
those days, and I was afraid of an extra
close scrutiny. At the same time I was
conscious of looking the most awful " out-
sider " and of not knowing in what form
to return the Admiral's welcome, whether
to take my hat off or shake hands or what.
On the top of this I saw my cousin stand-
ing staring at me from a few yards off,
and since I stood 6 ft. 5 in. in my socks I
was afraid he might observe me. Then I
became aware of another source of danger,

too, that was quite unexpected, for the captain of the ship also turned out to be a man with whom I was personally acquainted. I belonged at that time to a small club which took long country walks on Sundays, and the captain had several times joined in and spent whole days in our company. I knew, of course, that he was a Captain in the Navy, but did not know his ship.

The situation, then, was becoming very embarrassing, but I was saved by the naval officers' proverbial tact. Their cordiality was such that it put me at my ease at once and the inspection of the ship began.

I am afraid that my memory of the visit must necessarily refer mainly to my own experience, and it is rather scrappy, but a few moments seem to stand out specially. The first thing to do was to inspect the Guard of Honour, and this put the first strain on my powers of interpretation. There were two kinds of marines in the guard, and some of them had blue uniforms and some red, some were, I think, artillery and some infantry. The Admiral explained this to me and told me to pass it on to the Emperor. For a moment I boggled at this, I could not think what to say. "I am afraid it will be rather hard to put that into Abyssinian, sir," I said. "However, I'll try." "Entaqui, mahai, kustufani," I started, addressing Anthony Buxton, and whether those were real Swahili words learnt from the grammar, or whether they were invented on the spur of the moment, I don't remember, but they have stuck in my memory ever since. If they were real Swahili they were the only native African words that any of us used, and I could get no further. I don't find it easy to speak fluent gibberish impromptu, and I was again in something

of a difficulty. I must somehow produce
something that would not be too jerky,
and too unplausible. After a pause I began
again as follows: "Tahli bussor ahbat
tahl æsque miss. Erræma, fleet use . . ."
and so on. My language may have
sounded a bit odd, but at any rate I could
be fluent enough. When I was a boy I had
spent years on what is called a classical
education, and now I found a use for it.
It was the habit in the middle forms of my
school to learn by heart the fourth book
of Virgil's Æneid as "repetition." I was
able, therefore, to repeat whole stretches
of it, and I knew a good deal of Homer
in the same way. I was provided by my
education, then, with a fine repertory of
nonsense and did not have to fall back
entirely on my own invention. I had to
take care that neither the Latin nor the
Greek should be recognized, of course, but
I felt that probably few naval officers had

suffered an education like mine and, in any case, I so broke up the words and so mispronounced them that probably they would have escaped notice even of the best scholar. The quotation that I started with by the way is from the Æneid, Book IV, Line 437.

I found that my plan worked excellently, and even began to improve on it as in some emergencies that occurred more than once such as telling the Emperor to mind his head in a doorway, I would remember what I had said last time and use the same phrase again. This may have given us a little plausibility, especially as Anthony Buxton was very quick in picking up some of my words, and using them in his replies. I remember, though, hearing two officers who were eavesdropping behind some corner remark on the oddness of our lingo.

There was only one further precaution

that I had to take about our speech. Since there were two men on board, with one of whom, indeed, I had to converse a great deal, who might be expected to know my voice, some disguise was clearly necessary. Instead of my usual rather high register and Cambridge accent, therefore, I used a most unnatural deep bass, and an accent that was meant to be German. With that our disguise was as good as I could make it, but there was one other moment of suspense in connection with our speech, though I don't remember exactly when it occurred. Someone told me that there was one man in the Fleet who could speak to the Abyssinians in their own tongue, but mercifully added that he was away on leave.

The Admiral received us then and inspected the Guard of Honour with us, and then handed us over to Captain Y (my acquaintance) to be taken over the ship. I cannot remember now all that we saw, but I remember going down long corridors, looking at the wireless room, the sick bay if that is what it is called, and the Mess, having the big guns turned and aimed in different directions and so forth and so on. All these things I duly described in a mixture of Homer and Virgil.

As one might have expected the officers were almost too hospitable, and pressed us hard to eat and drink, but I was too afraid of the effect on our make-up. I excused us on the grounds that the religious beliefs of Abyssinia made it impossible for the Royal family to touch food unless it was prepared in quite special ways. The feeding problem was easily dealt with, but a worse moment was when I saw that Duncan's moustache was beginning to peel off. A slight breeze had got up, and a little rain began to fall, so that I was terrified what might happen

next. I did what I could with an um-
brella, but there were five people to cover,
and then I saw the obvious solution. I
spoke to the captain of the heat of the
Abyssinian climate and the chill of England, and he saw my point at once and
took us below. For a moment or two I
had to separate Duncan from the rest and
dab hastily at his upper lip, but I was able
to be quick enough to escape notice.

Another problem arose about a salute.
The Emperor of Abyssinia might expect
to be saluted by the firing of guns, and I
was consulted as to whether this should be
done. I took the course which I think at
any rate most of us approved of and said
that it was not necessary at all. The
French Fleet had not saluted us at Toulon,
why should the English ? The real fact
was that I understood that firing salutes
meant cleaning guns afterwards, and it
seemed too much of a shame to cause such

unnecessary trouble—besides, it was almost as grand to refuse a salute as to accept one.

After going all over the ship, there was nothing left but to return home. Cole who had been enjoying himself in the ward room rejoined the party, and we embarked again on our little steam launch.

We were accompanied again by a young officer, and I remember his pleasure at the astonishment of the simple natives when he switched on the electric light. I think it was this young man, too, who spoke to me about the tune with which the band had welcomed us. The bandmaster had been unable to get a copy of the Abyssinian National Anthem, but had played, as the next best thing, the Anthem of Zanzibar. I said I thought it did excellently, and considering Cole's and my history, I thought it did.

Another incident happened, I believe,

during this short passage to the shore, but I did not notice it—another vessel crossed our bows. But our launch contained Royalty and it is, apparently, a great breach of etiquette to cross the bows of Royalty, so the young officer who was responsible was had up by his Captain and reprimanded. Now the officer who was reprimanded was the young Prince of A. I had this story from another naval officer, and whether it is true or not I feel it ought to be.

When we reached the shore Cole tipped the sailors who came with us royally, and tried to pin a fancy-dress order on the breast of our young officer. He refused it rather shyly, saying he could not accept it without permission from his superiors. He was a nice young man, I thought, and I was really saddened a few years later when I saw what I believed to be his name in the list of those killed in some battle.

We drove to the station, then, and I think when we got into the train we were all except, perhaps, Cole, thoroughly exhausted. The only thing we could think of was our dinner, and luckily we were able to have it in our own compartment, so we ate it in comfort. We only kept up the hoax so far as to insist on the waiters wearing white gloves to serve us. I believe they had to dash out and buy them.

I suppose that most of us imagined that with our arrival home the whole incident was finished. We had decided not to tell the newspapers and, though something was bound to leak out, we did not expect what happened. We had had a photograph taken of ourselves in our fancy dress as a memento, and one day walking in the street I saw this reproduced on the poster of (I think) the *Mirror*. I believe that was how I first realized that someone had given the story away, and I have never felt the slightest doubt that it was Cole who did it, and he would certainly never contradict it.

After this we heard nothing more for some time, till one day walking with Cole near the top of Sloane Street, I saw Captain Y and his wife. He saw us, too, and recognized us and pretended at first to be horrified and then to call a policeman. After a second or two, though, he began to laugh and, in fact, took the whole affair in the best of good humours. There were certain other officers, however, who took it in a different spirit.

It was several weeks after the hoax was over when I was called down early one Sunday morning to see my cousin Z and found him waiting for me in the hall with an expression that I felt to be grim. He told me that he had come to find out just who had taken part in the hoax and that he wanted us all to apologize. He said that he already knew Cole's name, and that Virginia was involved, but he did not know who the others were. For my own part, I said, I did not mind apologizing in the least if it would make things easier for the Admiral. There had been questions asked in Parliament, and we had never meant to cause serious trouble, so if trouble could be avoided by an apology I should be quite ready to make one; though, of course, the others would have to be asked what they felt. My cousin asked me who the others were and, innocent as a lamb, I gave him their names. I, of course, had been hoaxed in my own turn, for the names were needed for another purpose.

My cousin almost snorted with contempt when I suggested that an apology might make things easier for the Admiral —as though such miserable creatures as the hoaxers could possibly make things easier or harder for such an exalted being as an Admiral. I gathered, though, what he minded even more than the questions of the gentlemen in Parliament was the behaviour of the little boys in the streets of Weymouth. When the hoax became so widely known as it did through the *Daily Mirror*, one of the newspapers published an interview. I think it was supposed to be with one of the assistants at Clarksons, who professed to know a great deal more than he did, and in particular stated that we had used the expression "Bunga-Bunga." Anyhow, the words "Bunga-Bunga" became public catchwords for a time, and were introduced as tags into music-hall songs and so forth. Apparently the Admiral was unable to go on shore without having them shouted after him in the streets, and I suppose that other officers suffered in the same way. Naturally, I was very sorry about this—we had no wish to make anyone really uncomfortable—and I expressed my sympathy to my cousin. He left me, then, but as he went he asked me whether I knew what the officers were saying about Virginia in the Mess. " They are saying that she is a common woman of the town—and *I* have to sit and hear this in silence." With this, holding his right hand in a marked way aloof from mine, he closed the door.

Of course, I got into touch at once with Cole, and then I heard his story. Things had gone very differently with him. The evening before my cousin and another naval officer had arrived at his house and asked to see him. Cole received them in his sitting-room, and they announced that they had come to avenge the honour of the Navy. They proposed to achieve this by beating him with a cane. In ordinary circumstances there would probably have been a free fight, and as Cole was pretty formidable, and as his manservant had scented trouble and was waiting outside the door in case he was needed, there is no telling who would have won. There was one thing which complicated matters, though. Cole was only just recovering from an illness which would have made violent exercise rather a serious danger. This was pointed out to the officers, and it put them in a dilemma. This was the third week-end, they said, that they had journeyed up to London to avenge the Navy, and they could not be foiled again. Eventually Cole made a proposal: he would agree to be beaten if he was allowed to reply in kind. This was agreed to, and the whole party adjourned to a quiet back street. Here they were safe from interruption, either from Cole's manservant or from the public, and here six ceremonial taps were administered to Cole's hindquarters, and six ceremonial taps were administered by him in return.

After this the Navy's honour was at least partly cleared, and the two sides shook hands and parted.

The only other adventure of this kind that I heard of was Duncan's. Whether Buxton or Ridley received visits from the Navy I never heard, and I have scarcely seen either of them since, but Duncan certainly did. He was sitting at breakfast with his father and mother one Sunday morning when a maid announced that some gentlemen had called to see him. It must have been the same morning that my cousin called on me, because Duncan had no warning, and went to see his friends who were waiting outside. Looking out of the window, Mrs. Grant saw her son tripped up and pushed into a taxi, the door slammed and the taxi driven off. She was naturally alarmed, and appealed to her husband to know what they should do. " I expect it's his friends from the *Dreadnought*," said Major Grant, with his usual beaming smile, and so, of course, it was. When he looked about him in the taxi Duncan found himself seated on the floor at the feet of three large men who were carrying a bundle of canes. They drove on for a bit in silence and Duncan asked where they were going. " You'll see plenty of ' Dreadnoughts ' where you are going," answered my cousin in an ominous voice. Then they asked Duncan whether he was ill, fearing, I suppose, a repetition of the night before.

At last they arrived somewhere in the region of Hendon, and here they stopped, and Duncan was told to get out and go into a field. There was no use in fighting against overwhelming odds, as Duncan said, and out he got and did as he was told.

" I can't make this chap out," said one

of the officers, " he does not put up any
fight. You can't cane a chap like that."
In the end it proved that they could cane
a chap like that, but only with some difficulty. My cousin was unable to do it
himself, but he could order his inferior
officer to do so and the inferior officer
could carry out his orders. Duncan, then,
received two ceremonial taps, also, and
the little party broke up. It so happened,
though, that Duncan had only his bed-
room slippers on, and no hat, and this so
distressed the officers that they pressed him
to accept a lift home.

" You can't go home like that," they
said, but Duncan felt it less embarrassing
to travel home by tube.

And now I come to what was, so far as
I know, the last episode. A great many
people—even those who had been thoroughly amused at the Cambridge joke—
were profoundly shocked at the idea of

hoaxing the Navy. I had an elderly relation, for instance, who had been delighted with the first hoax, and who kindly wrote offering his help in case there were legal proceedings in connection with the second. In his letter, however, he implored me "for God's sake" to "keep Virginia's name out of it," and felt bound to state his opinion that "His Majesty's ships are not suitable objects for practical jokes." Other people, and especially a certain military gentleman, began to ask questions in Parliament, and word came round to me that some form of reprimand was going to be administered to the Admiral. Whether the rumour was true I don't know, but it reached me apparently very directly from Mrs. McKenna, who was the wife of the First Lord of the Admiralty. It was suggested again that an apology might make things easier. If the hoaxers were to apologize that might appease those who

wanted the Admiral punished. When I
heard this, there was no time to waste.
Cole was either ill or away, and I could
not get hold of either Ridley or Buxton,
but I did get hold of Duncan, and together
we went down to Whitehall. The door-
keeper at the Admiralty seemed a little
surprised to see us, but when we told him
that we wished to see the First Lord about
the *Dreadnought* hoax he gave us an interested look and went to make inquiries.
We did not have to wait long, but were
taken upstairs to what I suppose was Mr.
McKenna's private room. Mr. McKenna
took it for granted at once that we had
come to beg for mercy. He told us that at
least one of us had committed a forgery
under the Post Office Acts, and was liable
to go to gaol and he at any rate had better
lie low, while the position of the rest of us
was doubtful. We tried to get him to see
that we were not in the least concerned

with what the Government proposed to do to us and were, indeed, extremely sceptical as to whether they could do anything at all. We were only offering, if he wanted it, an easy way of smoothing things over, but he would have none of it, and bundled us out. I think I really felt quite ill-used about this. We had come absolutely gratuitously to make what seemed a generous offer, and I did not see why this politician should treat us " de haut en bas," not even if he had rowed in the Cambridge boat before he was First Lord of the Admiralty. Perhaps, really, we had put him in an awkward position, and he did not know quite what to say; perhaps, indeed, he was laughing up his sleeve.

This was the end of the whole affair. I waited expecting to receive some sort of visitation from the Navy, but none came. Just why they beat Cole and Duncan, and not me, I have never understood. Anyone who does not know me may possibly think that it was because I was 6 ft. 5 in. high, and might have been a formidable customer. That is not so, however; if matters had come to a trial of strength I should have fallen a much easier victim than Cole. In any case, had I been a Goliath I am sure the Navy's gallantry would have risen to the occasion. I should be sorry, indeed, if anything I wrote were taken as intended to cast doubts on the bravery of naval officers. These men have very particular feelings on this point. Bravery is as much a matter of professional pride to them as is the quality of his potatoes to a greengrocer. I should be sorry without the strongest reasons to cast doubts on either.

Personally, I have always felt, as I expect most of those concerned did, that the officers' wisest course would have been that which the Vice-Chancellor recommended to the Mayor of Cambridge—to take no notice of us. As for " revenge," if they wanted any they had already had plenty before the hoax was over. They treated us so delightfully while we were on board that I, for one, felt very uncomfortable at mocking, even in the friendliest spirit, such charming people.